The Thrills

So Much For The City

A
B
EDITION

The Thrills
So Much For The City

GUITAR
TAB
EDITION

Wise Publications
part of The Music Sales Group

London / New York / Paris / Sydney / Copenhagen / Berlin / Madrid / Tokyo

Published by:
Wise Publications
8/9 Frith Street, London W1D 3JB, England.

Exclusive distributors:
Music Sales Limited
Distribution Centre, Newmarket Road,
Bury St. Edmunds Suffolk IP33 3YB, England.
Music Sales Pty Limited
120 Rothschild Avenue, Rosebery, NSW 2018, Australia.

Order No. AM978285
ISBN 1-84449-211-7
This book © Copyright 2003 by Wise Publications.

Music arrangements by Martin Shellard.
Music processed by Paul Ewers Music Design.

Printed in the United Kingdom

www.musicsales.com

SANTA CRUZ (YOU'RE NOT THAT FAR)

Words by Conor Deasy

Music by Conor Deasy, Kevin Horan, Pádraic McMahon,

Daniel Ryan & Ben Carrigan

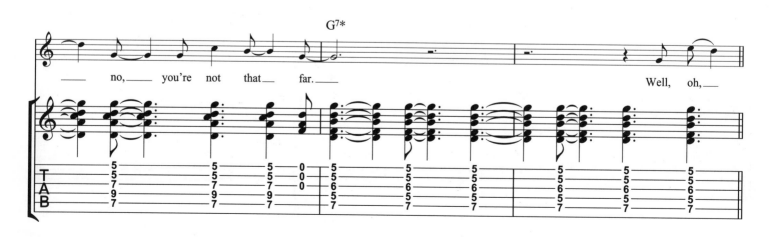

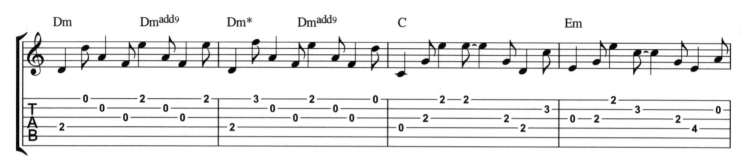

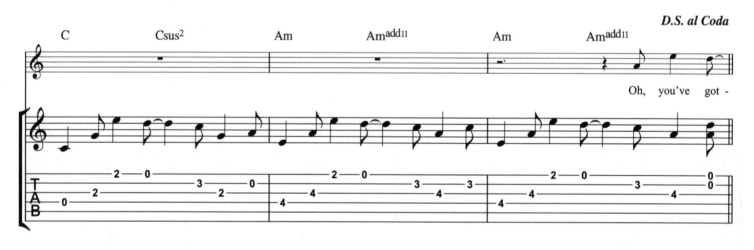

BIG SUR

Words by Conor Deasy
Music by Conor Deasy, Kevin Horan, Pádraic McMahon,
Daniel Ryan & Ben Carrigan

Contains elements from "Theme From The Monkees" –
Words & Music by Tommy Boyce & Bobby Hart

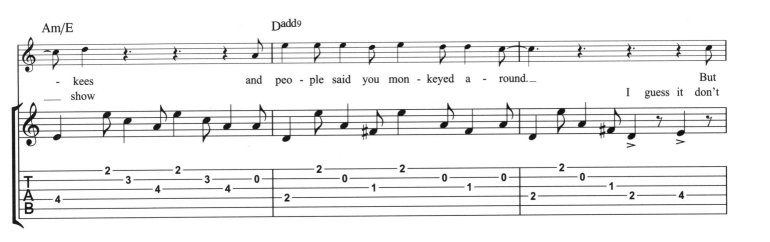

13

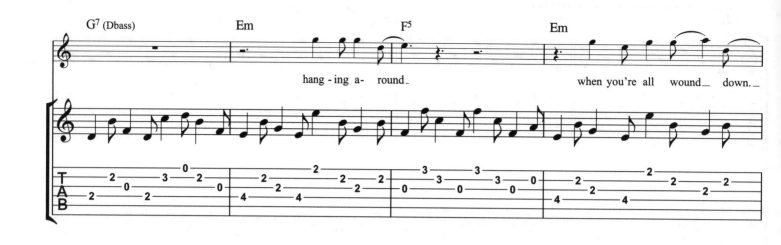

*chords implied by harmony

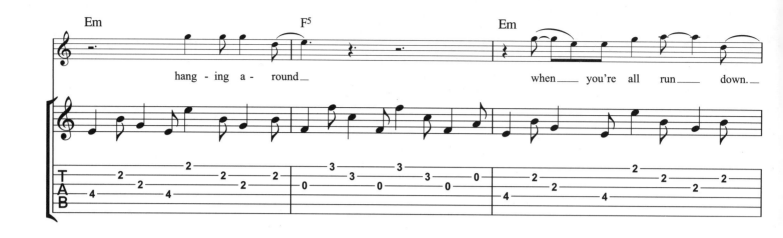

hang - ing a - round___ when___ you're all run___ down.

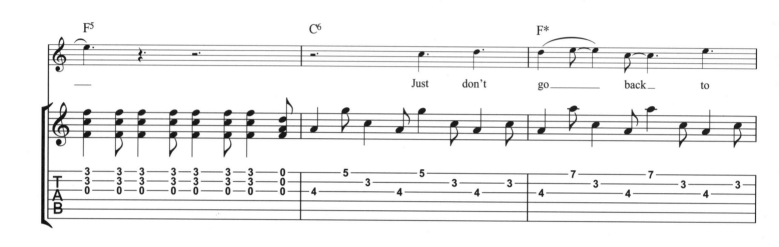

Just don't go___ back___ to

Big___ Sur___ oh, ba - by, ba - by please don't__ go,___ oh

ba - by, ba - by please don't__ go.___

ONE HORSE TOWN

Words by Conor Deasy
Music by Conor Deasy, Kevin Horan, Pádraic McMahon,
Daniel Ryan & Ben Carrigan

17

20

DON'T STEAL OUR SUN

Words by Conor Deasy
Music by Conor Deasy, Kevin Horan, Pádraic McMahon,
Daniel Ryan & Ben Carrigan

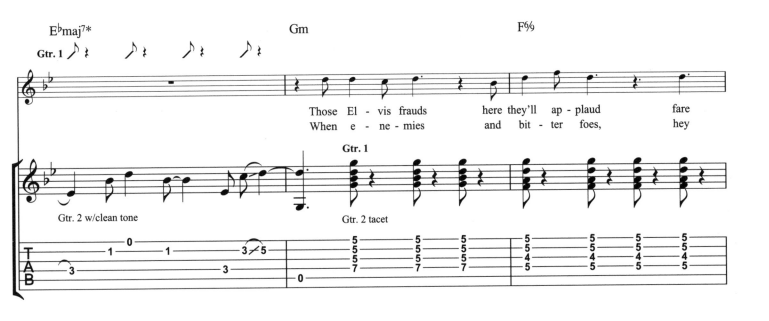

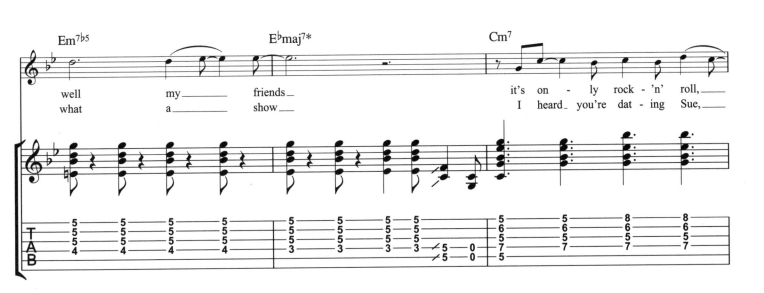

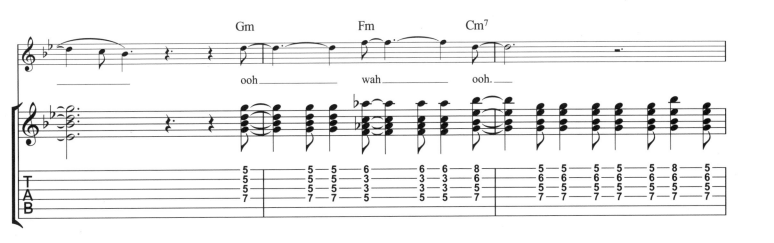

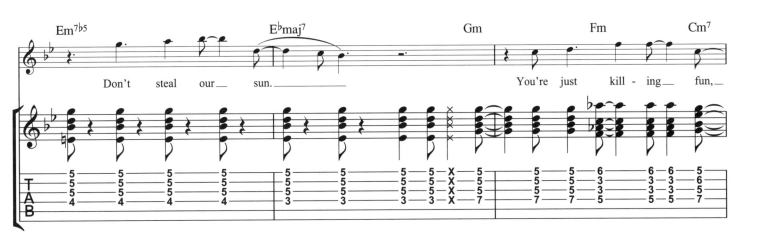

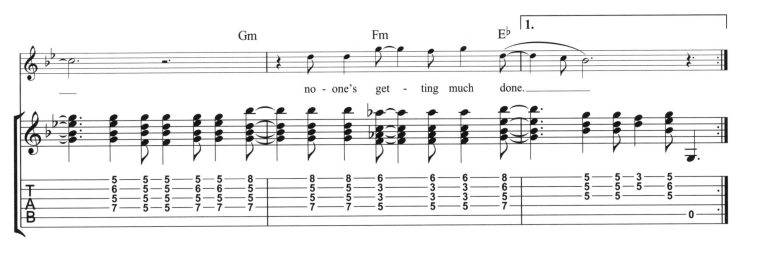

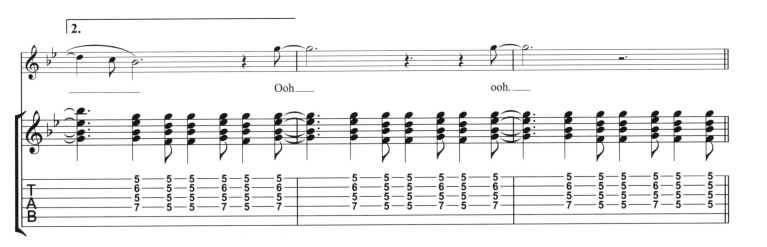

25

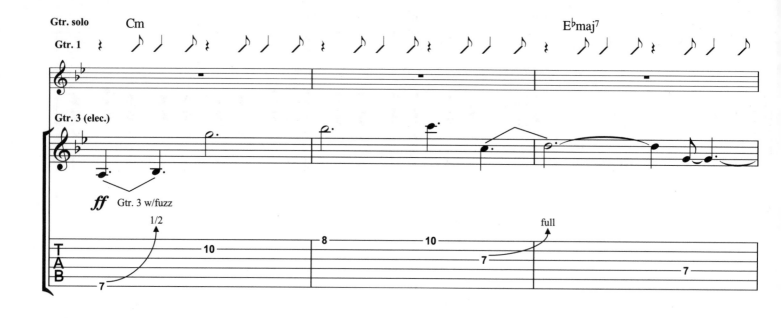

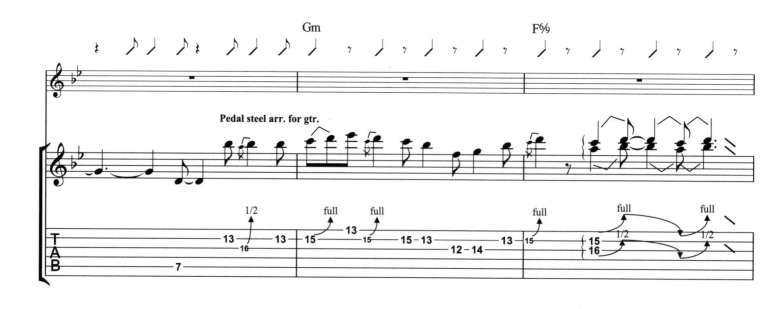

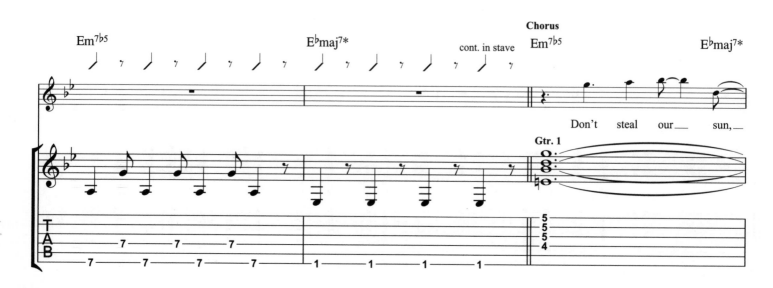

26

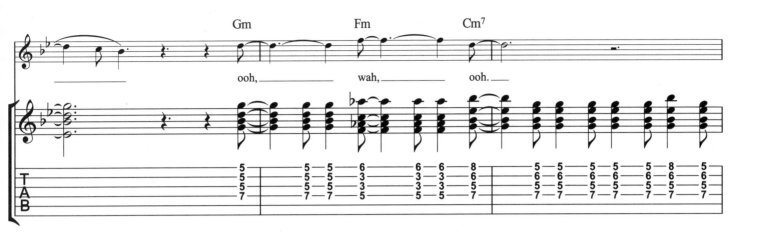

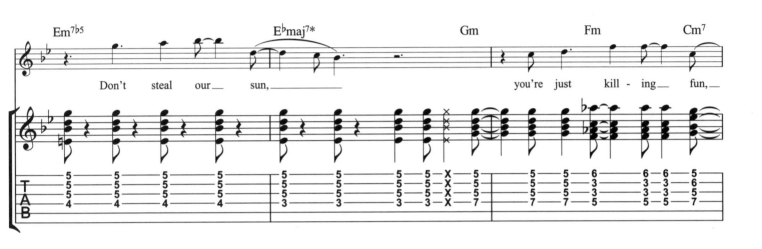

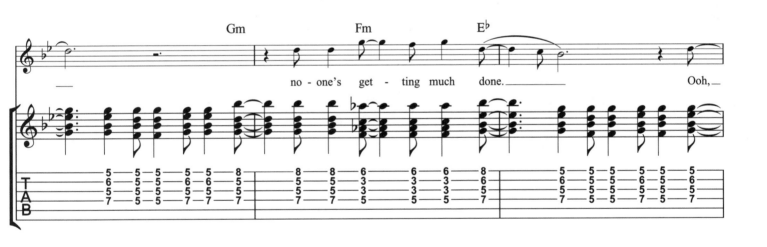

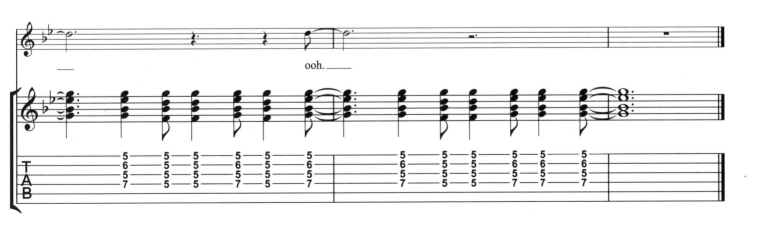

DECKCHAIRS AND CIGARETTES

Words by Conor Deasy
Music by Conor Deasy, Kevin Horan, Pádraic McMahon,
Daniel Ryan & Ben Carrigan

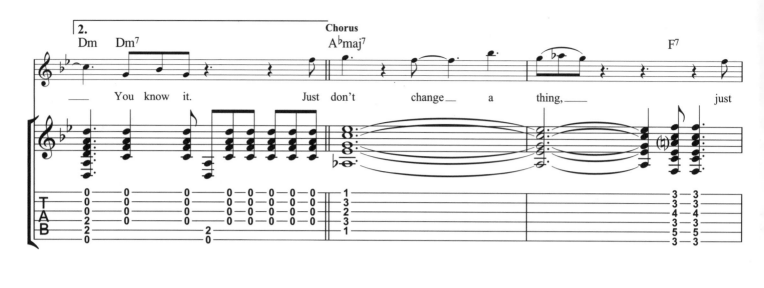

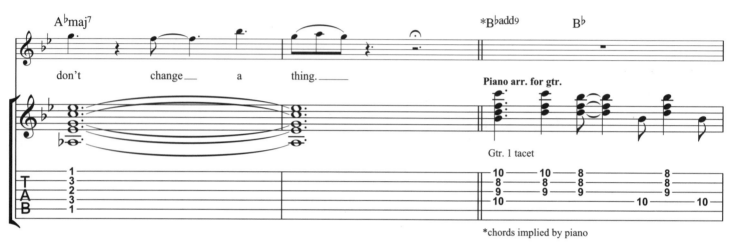

*chords implied by piano

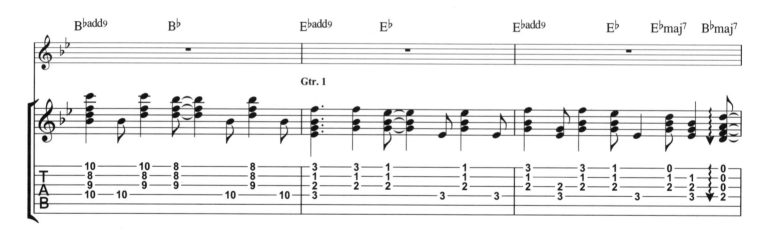

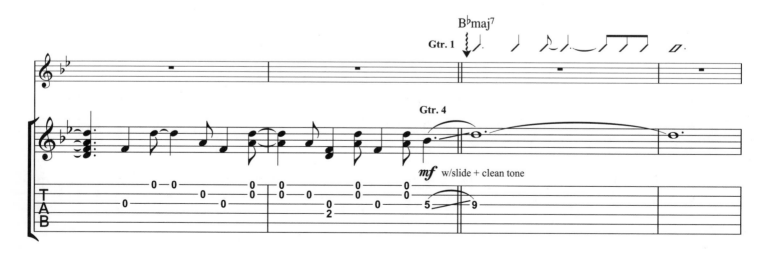

OLD FRIENDS, NEW LOVERS

Words by Conor Deasy
Music by Conor Deasy, Kevin Horan, Pádraic McMahon,
Daniel Ryan & Ben Carrigan

Eve - 'ry - bo - dy's talk - ing cra - zy, this town_ you're_
Bro - ken friend - ships sure - ly be - ckon,

*chords implied by harmony

SAY IT AIN'T SO

Words by Conor Deasy & Kevin Horan
Music by Conor Deasy, Kevin Horan, Pádraic McMahon,
Daniel Ryan & Ben Carrigan

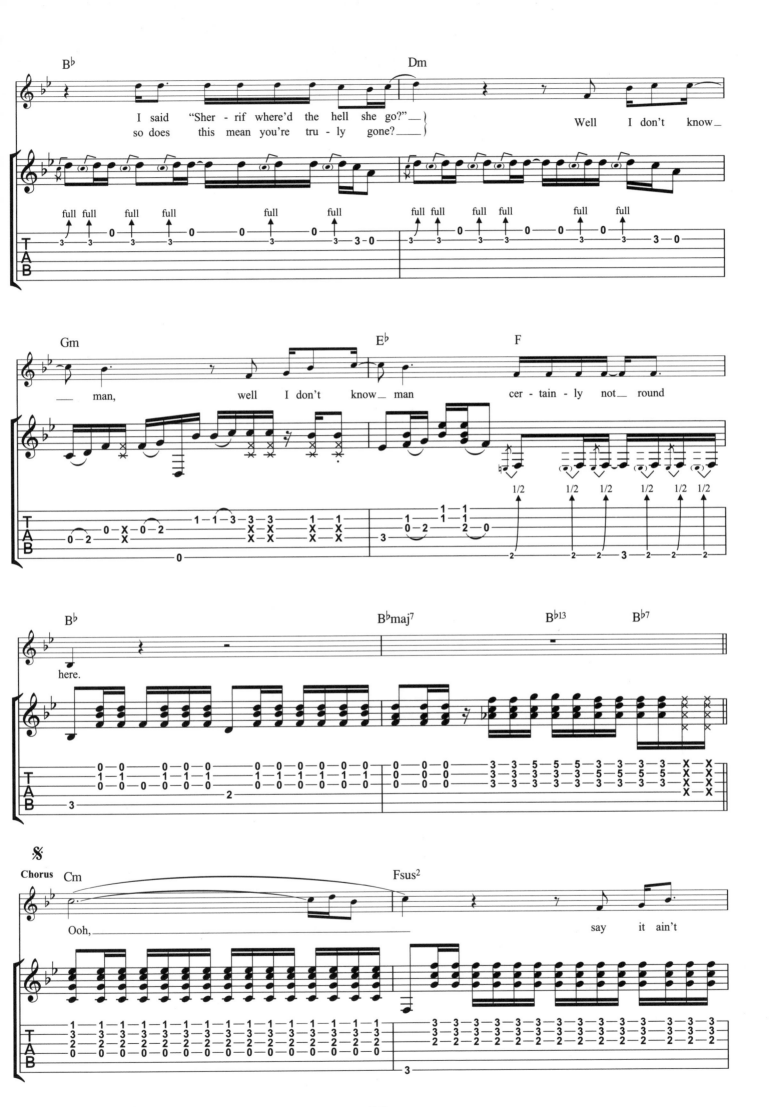

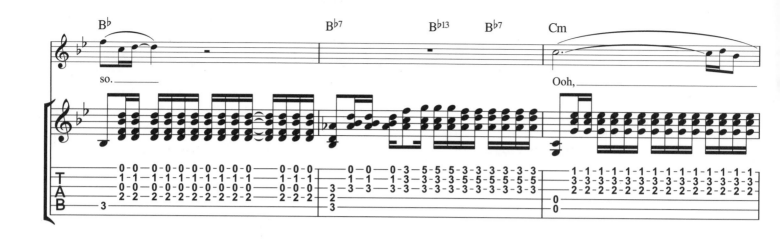

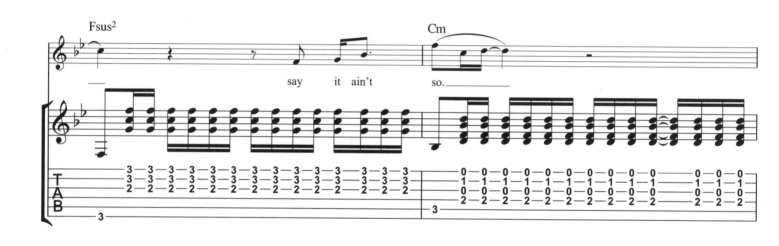

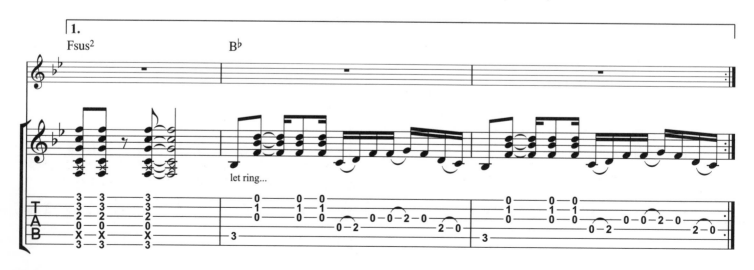

41

HOLLYWOOD KIDS

Words by Conor Deasy
Music by Conor Deasy, Kevin Horan, Pádraic McMahon,
Daniel Ryan & Ben Carrigan

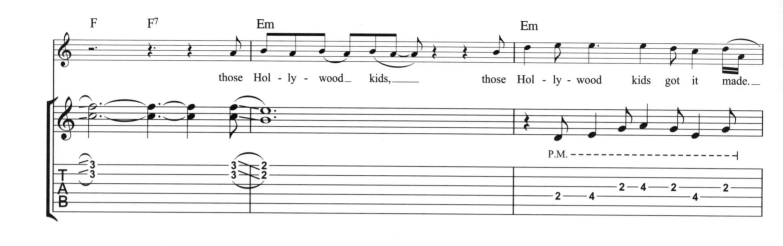

those Hol - ly - wood_ kids,_____ those Hol - ly - wood kids got it made.

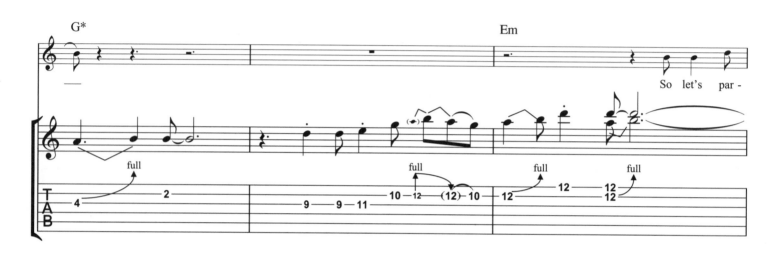

____ So let's par -

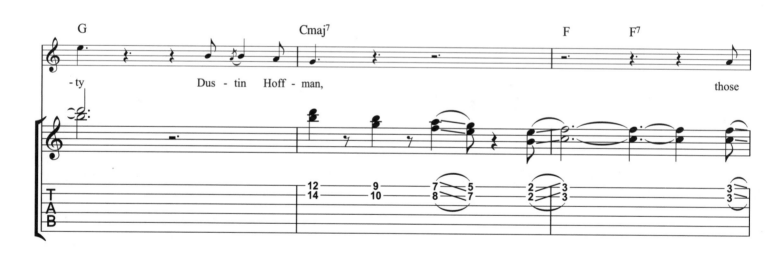

-ty Dus - tin Hoff - man, those

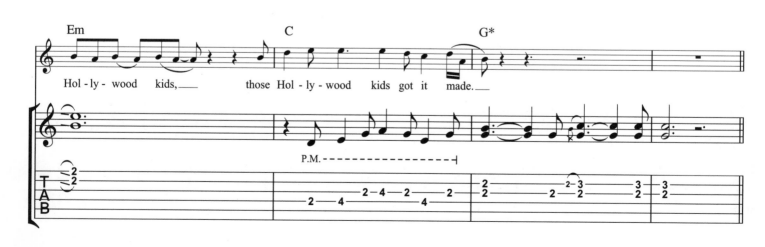

Hol - ly - wood kids,_____ those Hol - ly - wood kids got it made._____

45

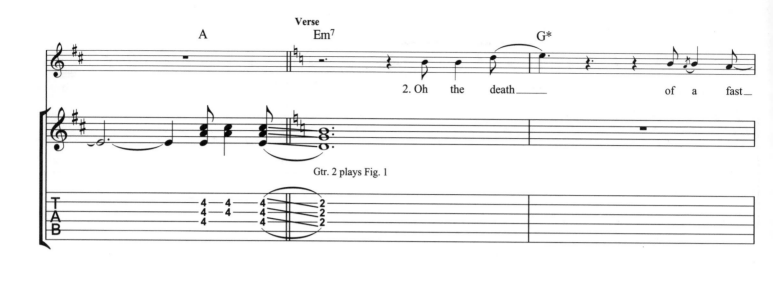

Gtr. 2 plays Fig. 1

2. Oh the death____ of a fast_

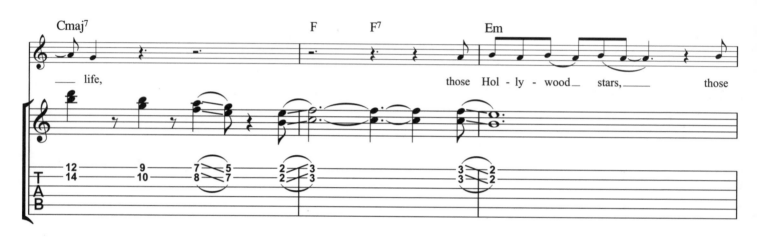

_ life, those Hol - ly - wood_ stars,____ those

Hol - ly - wood stars got - ta pay.____

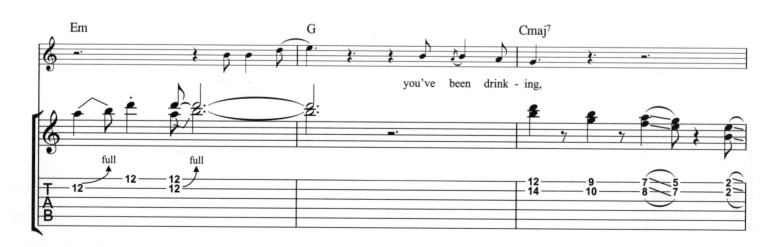

you've been drink - ing,

47

JUST TRAVELLING THROUGH

Words by Conor Deasy
Music by Conor Deasy, Kevin Horan, Pádraic McMahon,
Daniel Ryan & Ben Carrigan

This place suf- fo- cates

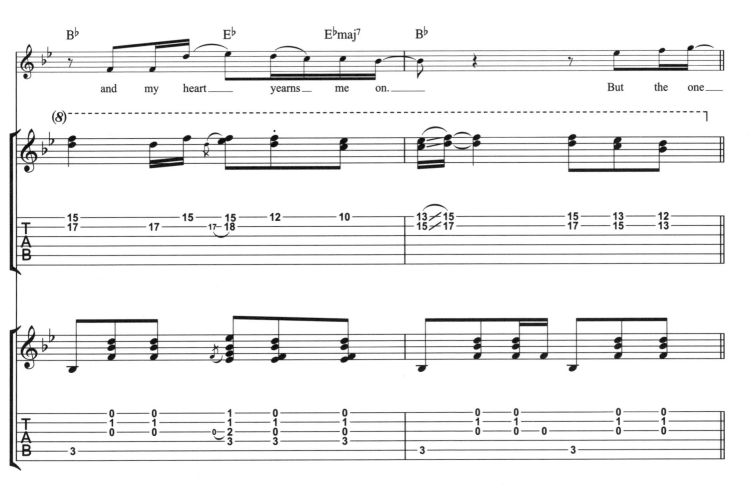

and my heart yearns me on. But the one

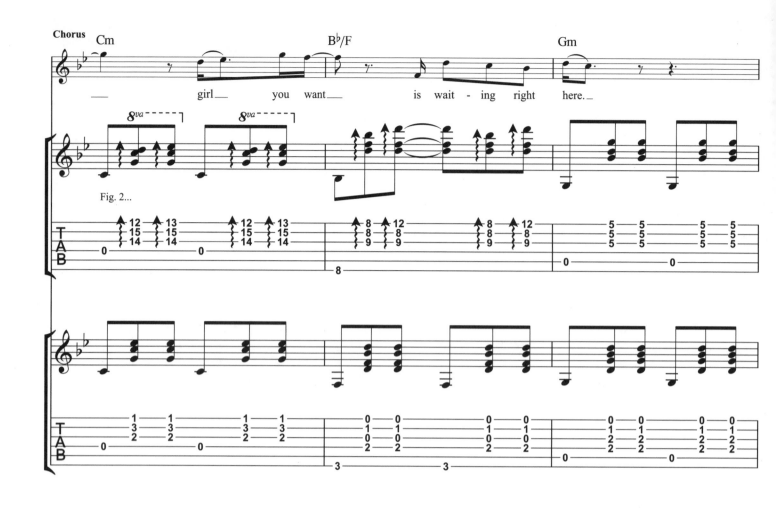

girl___ you want___ is wait - ing right here.___

Fig. 2...

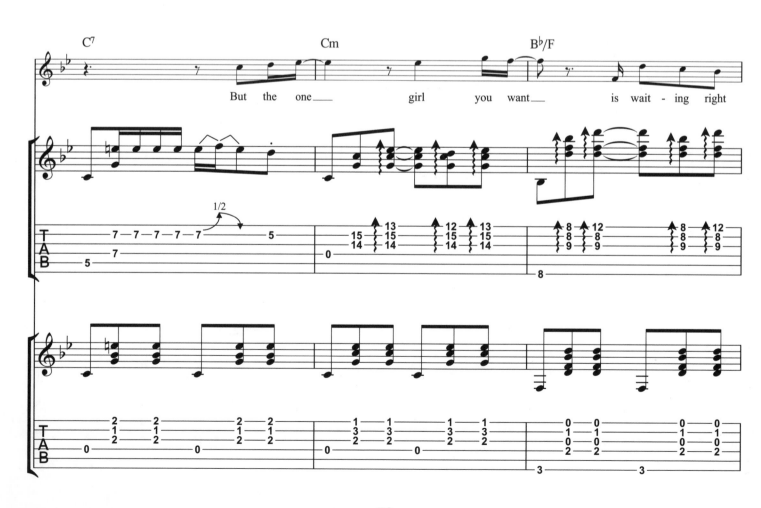

But the one___ girl you want___ is wait - ing right

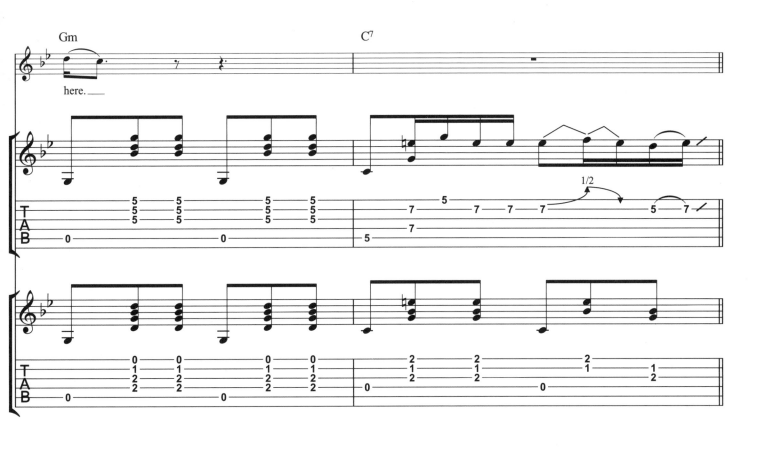

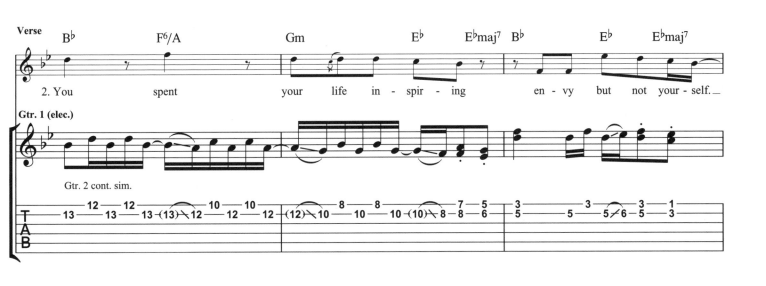

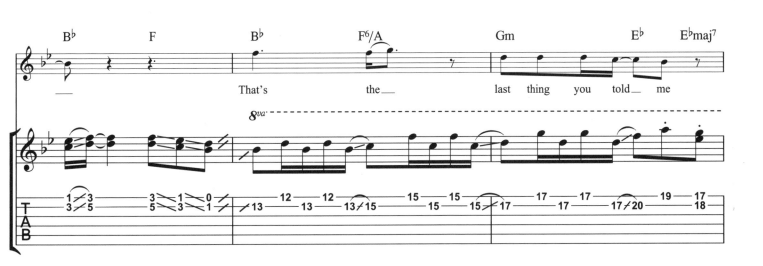

YOUR LOVE IS LIKE LAS VEGAS

Words by Conor Deasy
Music by Conor Deasy, Kevin Horan, Pádraic McMahon,
Daniel Ryan & Ben Carrigan

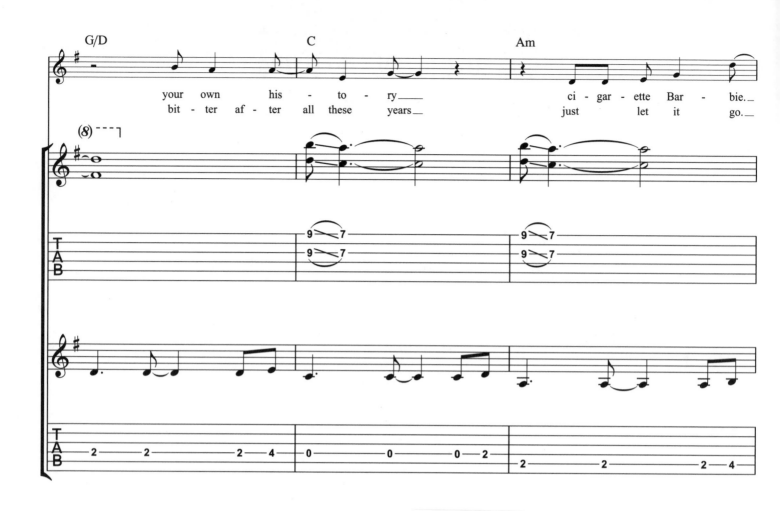

your own his - to - ry____   ci - gar - ette Bar - bie.____

bit - ter af - ter all these years____   just let it go.____

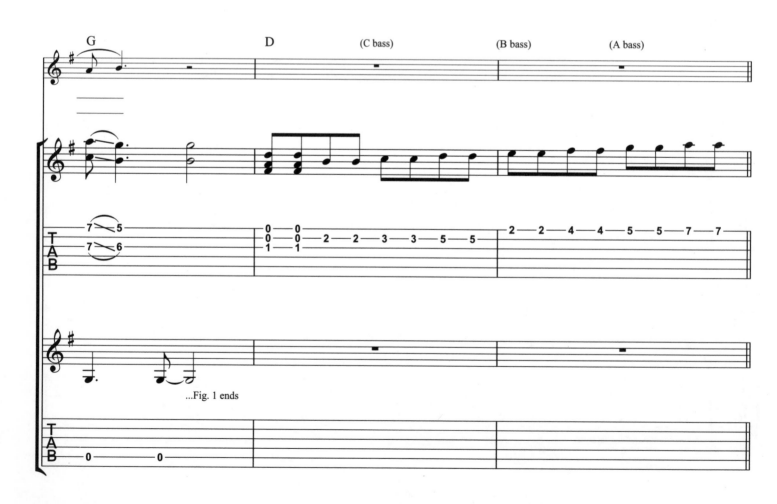

...Fig. 1 ends

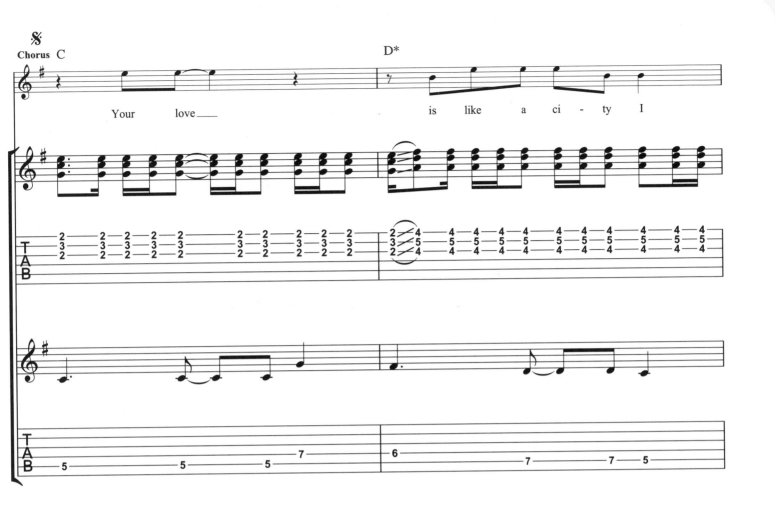

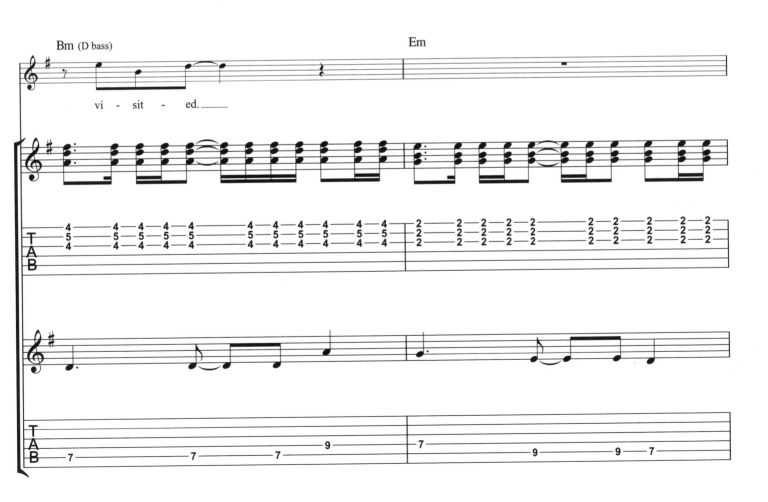

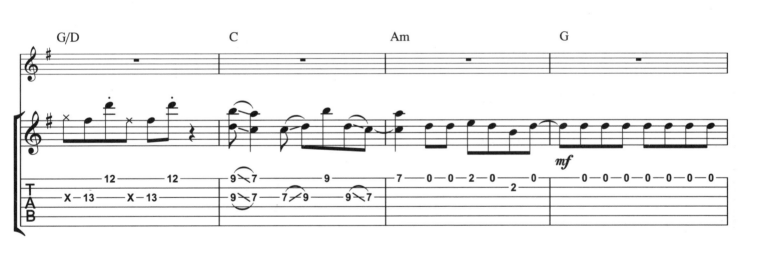

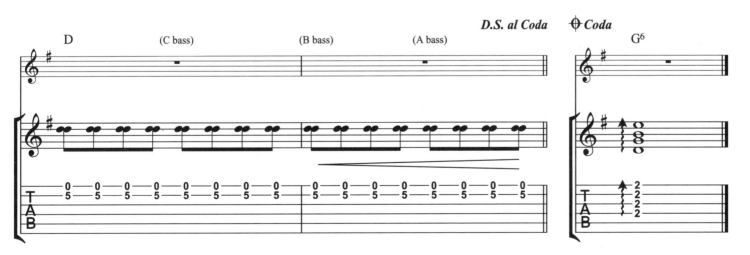

PLANS

Words by Conor Deasy
Music by Conor Deasy, Kevin Horan, Pádraic McMahon,
Daniel Ryan & Ben Carrigan

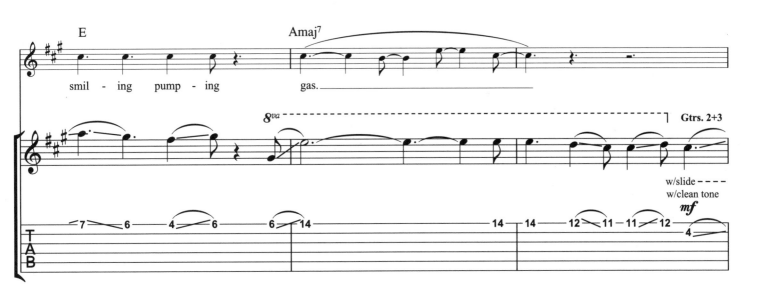

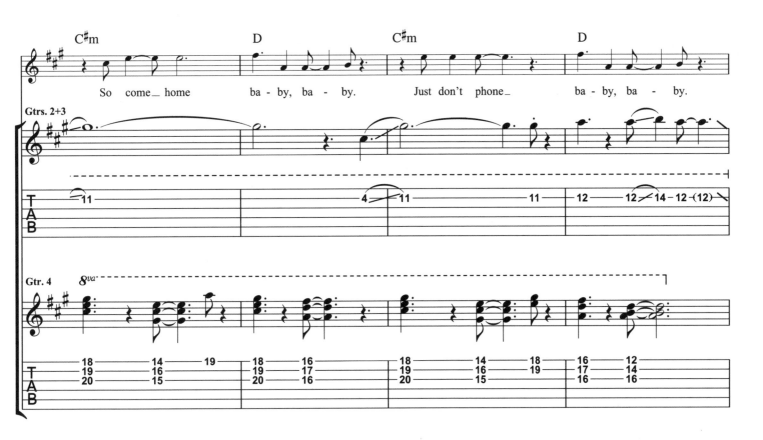

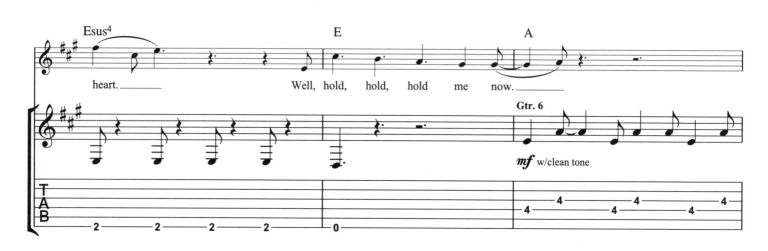

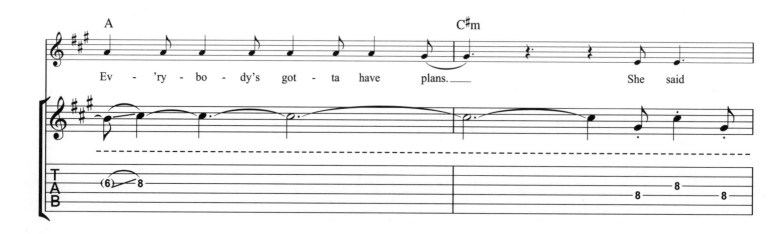

'TIL THE TIDE CREEPS IN

Words by Conor Deasy
Music by Conor Deasy, Kevin Horan, Pádraic McMahon,
Daniel Ryan & Ben Carrigan

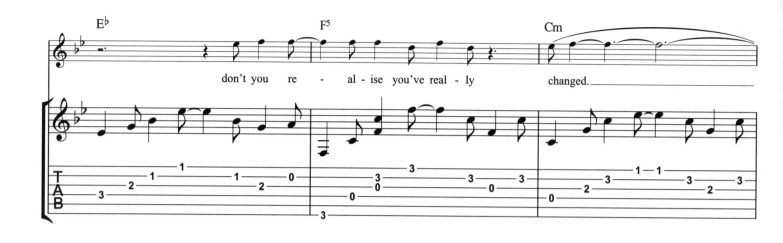

don't you re - al - ise you've real - ly changed._____

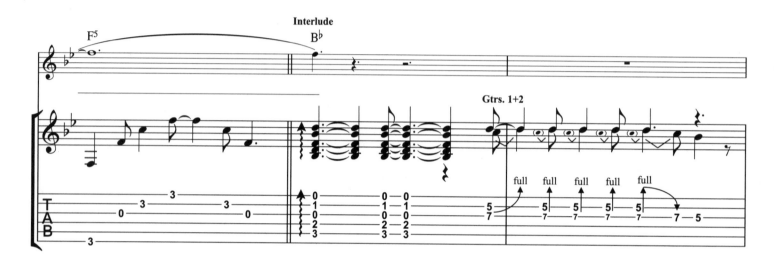

68

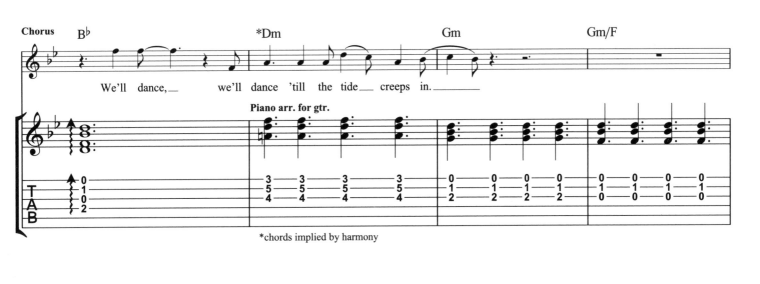

*chords implied by harmony

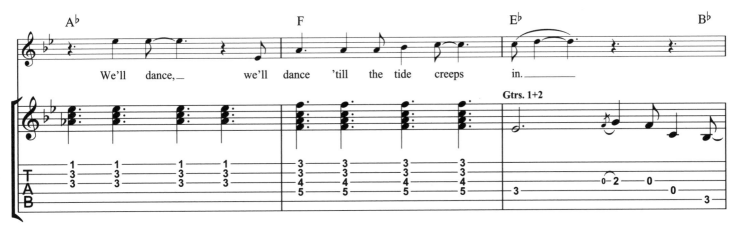

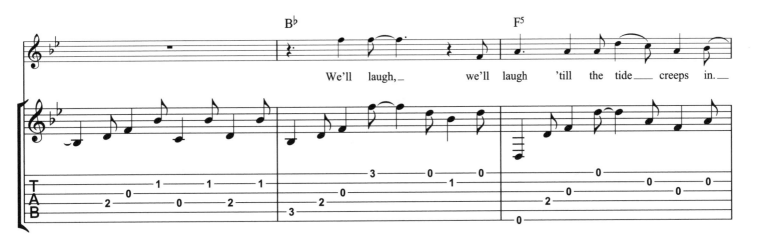

laugh   'till   the   tide   creeps   in.

GUITAR TABLATURE EXPLAINED

Guitar music can be notated three different ways: on a musical stave, in tablature, and in rhythm slashes.

RHYTHM SLASHES are written above the stave. Strum chords in the rhythm indicated. Round noteheads indicate single notes.

THE MUSICAL STAVE shows pitches and rhythms and is divided by lines into bars. Pitches are named after the first seven letters of the alphabet.

TABLATURE graphically represents the guitar fingerboard. Each horizontal line represents a string, and each number represents a fret.

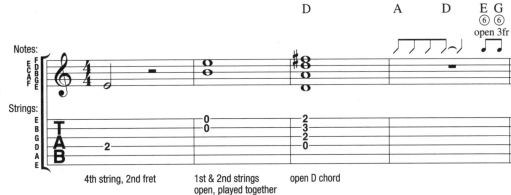

4th string, 2nd fret   1st & 2nd strings open, played together   open D chord

DEFINITIONS FOR SPECIAL GUITAR NOTATION

SEMI-TONE BEND: Strike the note and bend up a semi-tone (1/2 step).

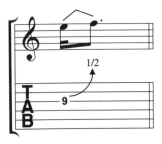

WHOLE-TONE BEND: Strike the note and bend up a whole-tone (whole step).

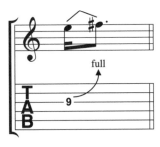

GRACE NOTE BEND: Strike the note and bend as indicated. Play the first note as quickly as possible.

QUARTER-TONE BEND: Strike the note and bend up a 1/4 step.

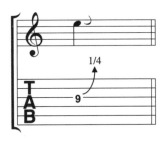

BEND & RELEASE: Strike the note and bend up as indicated, then release back to the original note.

COMPOUND BEND & RELEASE: Strike the note and bend up and down in the rhythm indicated.

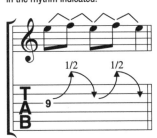

PRE-BEND: Bend the note as indicated, then strike it.

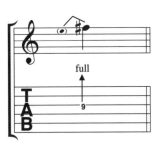

PRE-BEND & RELEASE: Bend the note as indicated. Strike it and release the note back to the original pitch.

UNISON BEND: Strike the two notes simultaneously and bend the lower note up to the pitch of the higher.

BEND & RESTRIKE: Strike the note and bend as indicated then restrike the string where the symbol occurs.

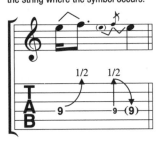

BEND, HOLD AND RELEASE: Same as bend and release but hold the bend for the duration of the tie.

BEND AND TAP: Bend the note as indicated and tap the higher fret while still holding the bend.

VIBRATO: The string is vibrated by rapidly bending and releasing the note with the fretting hand.

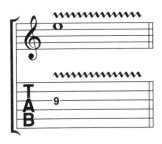

HAMMER-ON: Strike the first note with one finger, then sound the second note (on the same string) with another finger by fretting it without picking.

PULL-OFF: Place both fingers on the notes to be sounded, strike the first note and without picking, pull the finger off to sound the second note.

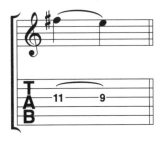

LEGATO SLIDE (GLISS): Strike the first note and then slide the same fret-hand finger up or down to the second note. The second note is not struck.

SHIFT SLIDE (GLISS & RESTRIKE):
Same as legato slide, except the second note is struck.

TRILL: Very rapidly alternate between the notes indicated by continuously hammering on and pulling off.

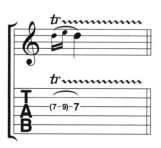

TAPPING: Hammer ("tap") the fret indicated with the pick-hand index or middle finger and pull off to the note fretted by the fret hand.

PICK SCRAPE: The edge of the pick is rubbed down (or up) the string, producing a scratchy sound.

MUFFLED STRINGS: A percussive sound is produced by laying the fret hand across the string(s) without depressing, and striking them with the pick hand.

NATURAL HARMONIC: Strike the note while the fret-hand lightly touches the string directly over the fret indicated.

PINCH HARMONIC: The note is fretted normally and a harmonic is produced by adding the edge of the thumb or the tip of the index finger of the pick hand to the normal pick attack.

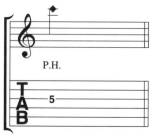

HARP HARMONIC: The note is fretted normally and a harmonic is produced by gently resting the pick hand's index finger directly above the indicated fret (in brackets) while plucking the appropriate string.

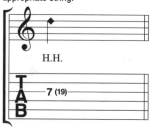

PALM MUTING: The note is partially muted by the pick hand lightly touching the string(s) just before the bridge.

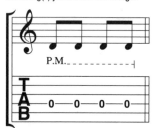

RAKE: Drag the pick across the strings indicated with a single motion.

TREMOLO PICKING: The note is picked as rapidly and continuously as possible.

ARPEGGIATE: Play the notes of the chord indicated by quickly rolling them from bottom to top.

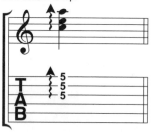

SWEEP PICKING: Rhythmic downstroke and/or upstroke motion across the strings.

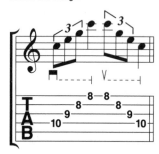

VIBRATO DIVE BAR AND RETURN: The pitch of the note or chord is dropped a specific number of steps (in rhythm) then returned to the original pitch.

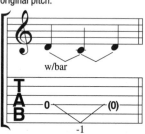

VIBRATO BAR SCOOP: Depress the bar just before striking the note, then quickly release the bar.

VIBRATO BAR DIP: Strike the note and then immediately drop a specific number of steps, then release back to the original pitch.

ADDITIONAL MUSICAL DEFINITIONS

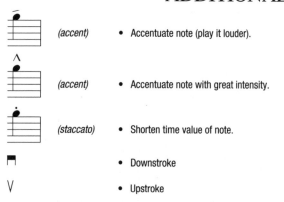

(accent)	•	Accentuate note (play it louder).
(accent)	•	Accentuate note with great intensity.
(staccato)	•	Shorten time value of note.
∏	•	Downstroke
V	•	Upstroke

D.%. al Coda

D.C. al Fine

tacet

NOTE: Tablature numbers in brackets mean:
1. The note is sustained, but a new articulation (such as hammer on or slide) begins.
2. A note may be fretted but not necessarily played.

• Go back to the sign (%), then play until the bar marked *To Coda* ⊕ then skip to the section marked ⊕ *Coda*.

• Go back to the beginning of the song and play until the bar marked *Fine*.

• Instrument is silent (drops out).

• Repeat bars between signs.

• When a repeated section has different endings, play the first ending only the first time and the second ending only the second time.

72